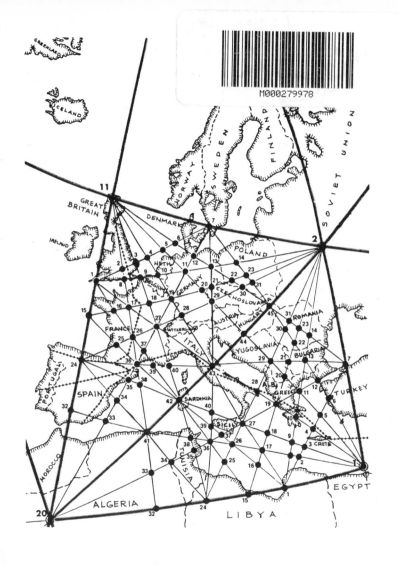

First published 2008
This revised edition © Hugh Newman 2014

Published by Wooden Books Ltd.
Glastonbury, Somerset

British Library Cataloguing in Publication Data
Newman, H.
*Earth Grids*

A CIP catalogue record for this book
may be obtained from the British Library

ISBN-10: 1-904263-64-x
ISBN-13: 978-1-904263-64-7

Designed and typeset in Glastonbury, UK.

Printed and bound using sustainable papers
by Violet Rose Ltd, China.

# EARTH GRIDS

## THE SECRET PATTERNS
## OF GAIA'S SACRED SITES

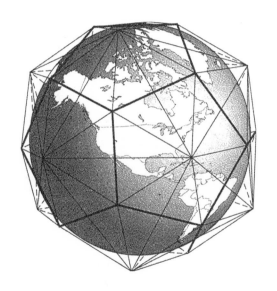

*Hugh Newman*

*I would like to especially thank my mother Meg Ketch, as well as Shaun Kirwan, Geoff Stray Bethe Hagens, Rand Flem-Ath, Robin Heath, Roy Snelling and my editor John Martineau. Thanks to the following for their illustrations: Bethe Hagens and William Becker for numerous images, Allan Holloway (p.25,41,55), Emmanuel Martin (p. 9, 44), Shaun Kirwan (p.7), Janet Lloyd Davies (p. 29). Thanks for image use to: Paul Devereux, John Michell, Ian Thompson, John Burke, David H. Childress, Rand Flem-Ath, David Zink, Bruce Cathie, Nicholas Mann, Richard Dannelly and Robert Coon. Images created from John Martineau's World Grid program and 'Google Earth' with Bethe Hagens' 'UVG grid' application.*

*Further reading: "The Atlantis Blueprint" by Rand Flem-Ath & Colin Wilson, "Anti-Gravity & the World Grid" ed. David Hatcher Childress, "The World Atlas of Mysteries" by Francis Hitchin, "The Energy Grid" by Bruce Cathie, and "the Measure of Albion" by John Michell and Robin Heath.*

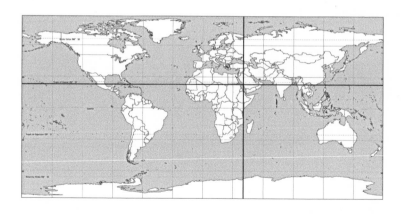

*Above: Mecca at the Golden Section of the French World Map. Golden latitudes occur at 21.25° North and South of the Equator. Mecca's latitude is 21.42° N, a mere 11.5 miles north of the Golden latitude. Golden longitudes occur 42.49° E and W of the moveable 0° meridian. Using the old 0° meridian through Paris the Golden meridian passes a mere 19 miles east of Mecca (after Martineau).*

# CONTENTS

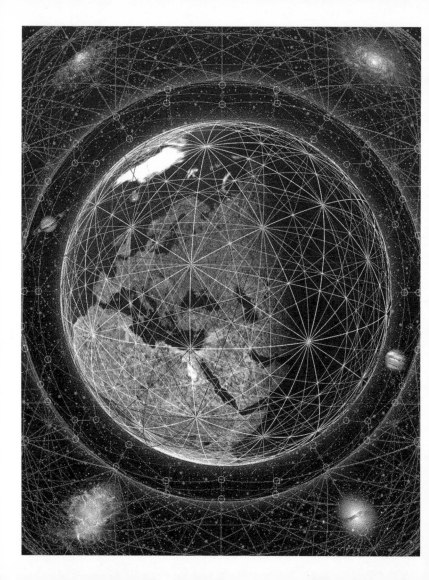

# INTRODUCTION

---

THE IDEA that there is, or even might be, an Earth grid seems far fetched to many people. But people have always wanted to know where they are on the planet, and the ancient system of longitude and latitude is one such grid, and we all still use it today.

The use of geometry is particularly widespread in the buildings of the ancient world, and modern grid researchers speculate as to whether the ancients, when siting their great temples, were aware not only of the local archaeoastronomy, but also of the relationship of their location to other important sites.

Nowadays we have electricity grids, water networks, phone systems and the internet, which criss-cross and surround us all. In the ancient world, the Chinese system of medicine described meridians of energy travelling through the body with acupuncture points at its nodes, and understood the Earth as having a similar network of energy lines.

The Earth today is seen as a living organism, and in the last thirty or so years, various books and articles have proposed Earth energy grids and the placement of ancient sites upon them. Indeed, the way they are placed around the planet suggest an informed and scientific project that was shared all around the globe in prehistory.

This book unravels the short history of grid research and takes another look at the distribution of sacred sites around the planet, revealing a remarkable network of surveying and megalithic engineering that supports the ancient idea of a geometric, or 'Earth-measured' worldview, which can now be seen as a new model for Gaia.

# THE EARTH

### *her structure, movement and natural energies*

---

The Earth is 4.57 billion years old, and life appeared on it within one billion years of its formation. Oxygenic photosynthesis began about 2.7 billion years ago, forming the atmosphere we enjoy today. The Earth is skinned in several major layers (*opposite top*).

Earth's outer surface is divided into massive tectonic plates that migrate across the surface due to continental drift. The planet once had just one large landmass and one great ocean. Today a mid-oceanic ridge runs around the entire planet, renewing the thin sea floor. In the mid-Atlantic, this ridge constantly erupts, pushing the Americas away from Europe and Africa (*below left*). Its current pattern in some areas resembles that of a dodecahedron (*below right*).

The equatorial radius of the Earth is 3,963.19 miles, 13 miles greater than the polar radius of 3,949.90 miles; the equatorial bulge resulting from the Earth's spin. Although the Earth changes over millions of years, it has remained basically the same during human civilisation.

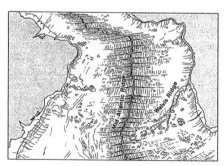

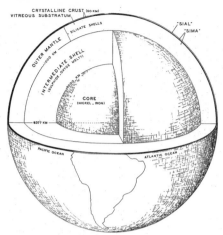

Left: The structure of the Earth. The crust descends merely 4 miles in the oceans, and 18-40 miles on land. The slowly flowing viscous mantle has a depth of about 1,800 miles (2,900 km). The core is thought to be liquid with a solid inner centre. The Earth's magnetic field derives from convection in the outer iron-rich core, combined with stirring caused by the Earth's rotation. The inner core of the Earth also rotates slightly faster than the rest of the planet. On the surface, fault lines, earthquake epicentres, geomagnetic forces and natural electrical (telluric) currents are all part of the traditional science of geomancy, today termed 'earth energy' and central to the idea of a world grid.

Right: The primary fault-line in the British Isles, along which earthquakes are most likely to occur. In the UK thunderstorms are much more frequent over areas with little or no faulting.

Below: The tectonic plates which make up the Earth's crust. Opposite left: The mid–Atlantic Ridge, formed by two plates pulling apart, and the roughly dodecahedral path it follows.

| Key | |
| --- | --- |
| MiF | Minch Fault |
| MT | Moine thrust |
| GGF | Great Glen Fault |
| GM | Glen Markie Fault |
| EL | Ericht-Laidon Fault |
| TF | Tyndrum Fault |
| KF | Killin Fault |
| LTF | Loch Tay Fault |
| OIF | Outer Isles Fault |
| HBF | Highland Boundary Fault |
| SUF | Southern Uplands fault |
| PeF | Pennine fault |
| MalF | Malvern fault |
| ChStF | Church Stretton fault |
| St-L | Sticklepath-Lustleigh fault |
| LizT | Lizard Thrust |
| DF | Dowsing fault |
| PoF | Poxwell fault |
| ET | Ebbor thrust |

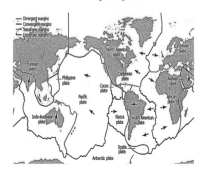

# THE GEOMAGNETIC FIELD

*electromagnetism and telluric energies*

The Earth's magnetic field takes a daily beating when struck by gusts of solar wind, as seen in the colourful 'Northern Lights'. The system is in flux. At dawn, the magnetic field lines (*opposite top*) shrink and surge through the land, our homes, our bodies and our brains each day. The field weakens at night then roars back to life every morning. At some natural places local geology makes this even stronger due to the effect of rocks, insulators (such as chalk) or the presence of water.

Magnetism and electrical force are two sides of the same coin. A moving electrical current generates a magnetic field, and a changing magnetic field generates electric current in anything present that will conduct it. The Earth itself is subject to the same forces—the field lines generate weak DC currents in the ground and, like all electric currents, these telluric energies travel better in some media than others. Ground containing a high level of metal or mineral-rich water conducts these natural, daily currents particularly well. Drier or less metallic ground conducts it less well. When these two types of land intersect, a 'conductivity discontinuity' occurs. Interestingly, this is also where many ancient sites seem to be located and often where anomalous 'balls of light' are seen.

'BOLs' are created by natural electrical charge from the sudden drop in the magnetism of the field lines. At Stonehenge and other ancient sites, a henge cut over three feet into the ground resists this telluric energy, directing it through the entrance, building up electrical charge within the site. Is this one of the lost technologies of the ancients? Were they harnessing it worldwide into a planetary grid of energy?

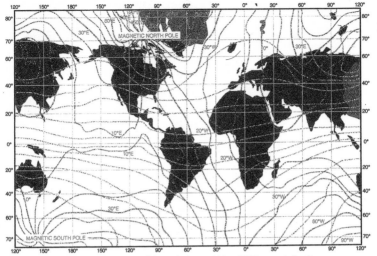

Above: Magnetic Currents of the Earth, showing N-S and E-W magnetic flow lines.

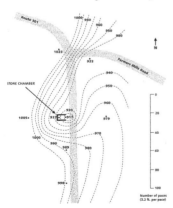

Above: Geomagnetic contour map of a Native American rock chamber in Kent Cliff, New York, showing magnetic anomaly at the doorway (J. Burke).

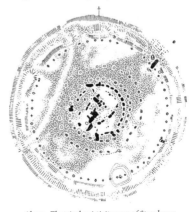

Above: Electrical resistivity map of Stonehenge. Darker areas show where more natural electrical current has travelled through the Earth (J. Burke).

# LEYS AND DRAGON LINES
*landscape alignments and lines of force*

A network of landscape alignments was discovered in the 1920s by Alfred Watkins. Alignments consisting of five or more sacred sites, whether churches, megaliths, springs or hilltops, he termed "leys". A particularly long ley was unveiled by John Michell in the late 1960s. He named it the St. Michael Line because it plotted numerous sites dedicated to St. Michael, as well taking in ancient sites such as Avebury and Glastonbury Tor. Michell noticed it also aligned to Beltane (Mayday) sunrise and Samhain (Halloween) sunset. Twenty years later, Hamish Miller and Paul Broadhurst dowsed two great energy currents weaving like serpents around the St. Michael Line, never following it precisely, but meeting at major node points along it. They even found it continuing in St. Petersburg, Russia, suggesting a planetary current.

Traditions of straight alignments exist in Peru, Bolivia and in the far-East, where Feng-Shui practitioners know them as 'Dragon lines', while in Australia the Aborigines talk of 'Song-lines'. In 1939, Josef Heinsch noted that many ancient sites in Germany were arranged in grids over vast distances and large circular and triangular patterns exist in Britain (*opposite page*). Theories of the origin of such formations range from underground water streams, geological fault lines, spirit paths to navigational tools left by ancient alien astronauts.

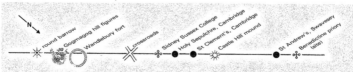

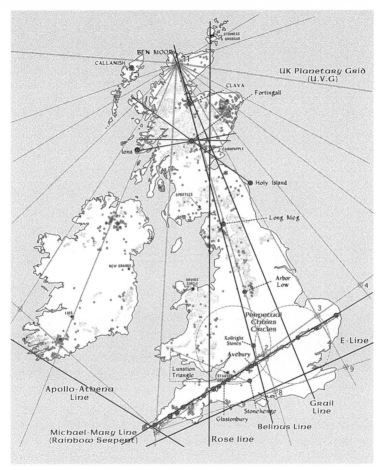

*Above: A selection of long leys, landscape geometries and Earth energies (by Newman & Kirwan). The map also marks megalithic sites, 'the Lunation Triangle' (after R. Heath) and the 'Circles of Perpetual Choirs' (after J. Michell). Some of these lines neatly correspond to the Earth grid and ancient geodetic measurement systems. Shorter leys have been omitted, but as an example the 'Cambridge ley' can be seen on the left page.*

7

# GRID BEGINNINGS
*early evidence of global patterns*

---

> *"A great scientific instrument lies sprawled over the entire surface of the globe. At some period – perhaps it was over 4,000 years ago – almost every corner of the world was visited by a group of men who came with a particular task to accomplish. With the help of some remarkable power, by which they could cut and raise enormous blocks of stone, these men erected vast astronomical instruments, circles of erect pillars, pyramids, underground tunnels, cyclopean alignments, whose course from horizon to horizon was marked by stones, mounds, and earthwork…The vast scale of prehistoric engineering is not yet generally recognised."*

These words of John Michell in his seminal *The View Over Atlantis* suggest a very ancient grid system of the Earth, and similar quotes from the distant past support this. For example *The Book of Enoch*, rediscovered in 1773 by James Bruce, is interpreted as describing a great survey of the Earth in prehistoric times:

> *"And I saw in those days how long cords were given to the Angels, and they took themselves wings and flew, and went towards the north. And I asked an Angel, saying unto him: 'Why have these taken cords and gone off?' And he said to me: 'They have gone to measure.'"*

Druid legends talk of twelve great 'courts' that encircle the globe, and a Hopi creation myth describes how the creator Tiowa assigned Spider Grandmother Woman to send sound and cosmic energy to the crystal at the centre of the Earth to bounce back to the surface and create 'spots of the fawn', or sacred power centres joined together by a lattice of energy. A Brule Sioux creation myth describes the Sun empowering the planets, orbits and stars to "come to the sixteen  hoops", suggesting a network of great Earth circles over the planet.

A Hopi Creation Myth describes how the Creator Tiowa assigned Spider Grandmother Woman (Kokyanwuhti) as the Earth's guardian. She spat into two handfuls of Earth and created Poqanghoya and Palongwhoya (and later, Hicanavaiya, Man-Eagle, Plumed Serpent and many others). The two brothers linked minds. Poqanghoya was sent to the north pole, where he gave structure and form to life. Palongwhoya went to the south pole, to say prayers and tune in to the heartbeat of Tiowa. When the two beats were in perfect harmony, a surge of life force came shooting down to the crystal at the centre of the Earth. When the sound hit the crystal, the energy shot out in all directions, channeled by the structural magic of Poqanghoya. The reflected life-energy then popped from the Earth's crust, bringing the planet to life. At some places this energy is said to be more abundant.

# DYMAXION MAPS
*Buckminster Fuller's cut-out globes*

---

In the 1940s Buckminster Fuller created several world maps in his attempts to create a visually accurate, flat rendition of a spherical globe. In 1946 he patented the Dymaxion Projection based on the cubeoctahedron (*opposite top*). A later 1954 version called *The AirOcean World Map* used a slightly modified icosahedron (*shown below*). Each face of these polyhedra is a gnomonic projection (displaying great circles as straight lines), and on both maps, the landmasses are accurately rendered, unlike other flat projections of the Earth which distort either shape, area, distance or directional measurements. On the Mercator world map, for instance, Greenland appears to be three times its corresponding globe size, and Antarctica appears as a long thin white strip along the bottom edge of the map. Even the popular Robinson Projection, used in many schools, shows Greenland distorted to 60% larger than its corresponding globe size.

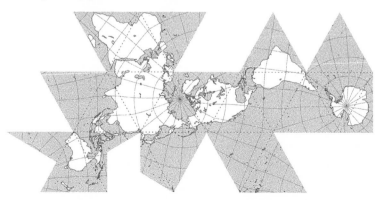

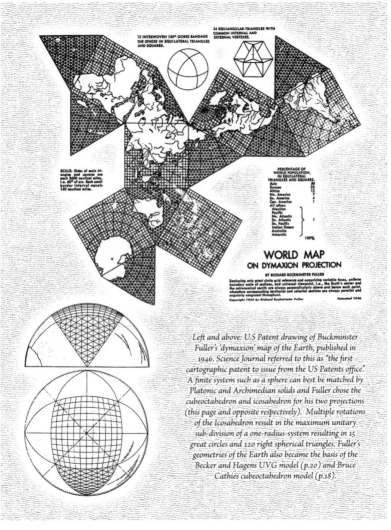

12 INTERWOVEN 180° GORES BANDAGE
THE SPHERE IN EQUILATERAL TRIANGLES
AND SQUARES.

24 EQUIANGULAR-TRIANGLES WITH
COMMON INTERNAL AND
EXTERNAL VERTEXES.

SCALE: Sides of main tri-
angles and square are
each 3600 nautical miles,
i.e. 60° of arc. Each small
border interval equals
180 nautical miles.

| PERCENTAGE OF WORLD POPULATION IN EQUILATERAL TRIANGLES AND SQUARES. | |
|---|---|
| Asia | 50 |
| Europe | 26 |
| Africa | 12 |
| No. America | 5 |
| So. America | 4 |
| Cen. America | 1 |
| All others | |
| Pacific | |
| Aleutian | |
| No. Atlantic | |
| So. Atlantic | |
| So. Pacific | |
| Indian Ocean | 1 |
| Australia | |
| Antarctic | |
| | 100% |

# WORLD MAP
## ON DYMAXION PROJECTION

BY RICHARD BUCKMINSTER FULLER

Employing only great circle grid reference and comprising variable focus, uniform
boundary scale of sections, and universal viewpoint, i.e., the Earth's center and
the astronomical zenith are always perpendicularly above and below each point,
wherefore corresponding territorial and celestial sections are always parallel and
angularly congruent throughout.

Left and above: U.S. Patent drawing of Buckminster
Fuller's 'dymaxion' map of the Earth, published in
1946. Science Journal referred to this as "the first
cartographic patent to issue from the US Patents office."
A finite system such as a sphere can best be matched by
Platonic and Archimedian solids and Fuller chose the
cubeoctahedron and icosahedron for his two projections
(this page and opposite respectively). Multiple rotations
of the Icosahedron result in the maximum unitary
sub-division of a one-radius-system resulting in 15
great circles and 120 right spherical triangles. Fuller's
geometries of the Earth also became the basis of the
Becker and Hagens UVG model (p.20) and Bruce
Cathies cubeoctahedron model (p.18).

# THE PLATONIC SOLIDS
*timeless polyhedra in ancient days*

Each of the five Platonic Solids (*opposite*) is made up of faces of just one regular polygon, with all vertices lying on a sphere. Their perfect symmetry makes them an integral part of planetary grid research. The tetrahedron has four vertices and four triangular faces, the octahedron six vertices and eight triangular faces, the cube eight vertices and six square faces, the icosahedron twelve vertices and twenty triangular faces, while the dodecahedron has twenty vertices and twelve pentagonal faces. The earliest written evidence of them goes back to the era of Pythagoras and Plato [427-347 BC]. Plato writes in the *Phaedo* [110b]:

> *"The real Earth, viewed from above, resembles a ball made of twelve*
> *pieces of leather, variegated and marked out in different colors ..."*

This appears to reference a dodecahedron. It is certainly the first mention of the Earth grid. In the *Timaeus*, he also says the Demiurge used a twelve-sided form as a pattern for the World.

However, hundreds of neolithic carved stones, discovered in Northern Scotland and Europe (*see below*), perfectly resemble the Platonic solids (and date to 2,000 years before Plato). Geometer Keith Critchlow believes that they could have been used to map the stars, function as navigational aids or act as props to teach students spherical geometry.

*Octahedron*

*Icosahedron*

*Dodecahedron*

*Tetrahedron*

*Cube*

Above: The Tetrahedral and Cube-Octahedral system, common in crystals and widely used in architecture. The three Platonic solids which embody this system are shown. This system contains numerous root √2 and √3 proportions.

Left: The Icosi-Dodecahedral grid. Above left: The Icosahedron. Above right: The Dodecahedron. The Icosahedron and the Dodecahedron are each other's duals, which is to say that each is constructed from the centres of the other's faces.

Above: The Icosi-Dodecahedral system, common in viruses, pollens, plankton and other living things. Two Platonic solids embody this system, which is rich is golden section proportions.

13

# VILE VORTICES
*vanishing aircraft and time dilations*

---

In the early 1970s Ivan T. Sanderson, a biologist and author, plotted ship and aircraft disappearances worldwide, and noticed twelve especially peculiar areas equally spaced over the globe (including the north and south pole). In these 'hot spots' magnetic anomalies, unexplained disappearances, mechanical and instument malfunctions and other energy aberrations all seemed to congregate.

One of the zones was on the western tip of the Bermuda Triangle, an infamous area off the coast of Florida, extending from Bermuda to the tip of southern Florida, and then to the Bahamas via Puerto Rico. Over 100 aircraft disappearances and about 1,000 lost lives have been reported in the Bermuda Triangle since 1945.

In his 1972 article *Twelve Devil's Graveyards around the World*, Sanderson described how statistical research and modern communications technology had helped him discover other areas with similar anomolies, such as the Dragon's Triangle (or Devil's Sea) off the south-east coast of Japan. Between 1950 and 1954, nine large ships completely disappeared in this area and UFO sightings as well as magnetic anomalies have often been reported there. This area is also along the rim of the 'Ring of Fire', the highly active volcano chain of the Pacific.

When Sanderson drew the hot spots on a map, he noticed that the twelve areas were spaced equally apart and neatly formed the vertices of an icosahedron with most of them in the sea.

Sanderson was later accused of selecting data to fit his theory, but his work remains a tantalising glimpse of a planetary grid at work.

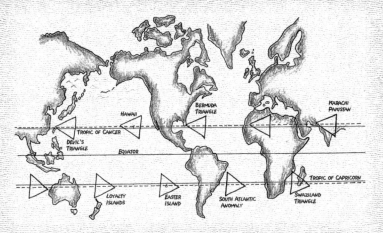

The twelve "Devil's Graveyards". Note how they fall on the Tropic of Cancer and the Tropic of Capricorn (apart from the north and south poles). Disappearances, mechanical and instrument malfunctions and many cases of time dilations, light phenomena and magnetic variations have been reported in these areas.

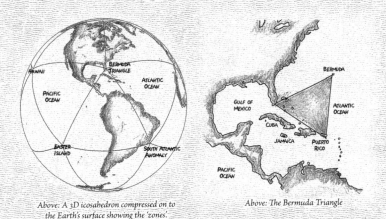

Above: A 3D icosahedron compressed on to the Earth's surface showing the 'zones'.

Above: The Bermuda Triangle

# RUSSIAN DISCOVERIES
*the crystal core and the dodecahedron*

---

Around the same time as Sanderson's work, an article was published in Moscow in 1973 stating that the Earth could have started out as an angular crystal and only formed into a sphere after hundreds of millions of years. Edges of the great crystal could still be preserved within the planet with its energies still recordable on the surface. Nikolai Goncharov, a Muscovite historian, took the idea a step further by proposing a dodecahedron aligned to the axial north/south poles and the mid-Atlantic ridge. He then mapped ancient cultures onto a globe to discover a geometric pattern. Next, with Vyacheslav Morozov, a linguist, and Valery Makarov, an electronics specialist, he published *Is the Earth a Large Crystal?* in *Chemistry and Life*, the popular science journal of the USSR Academy of Sciences. They then matched Sanderson's idea by placing an icosahedron within it.

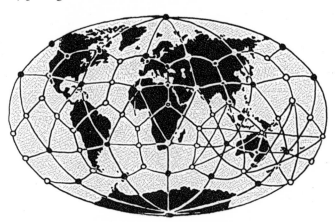

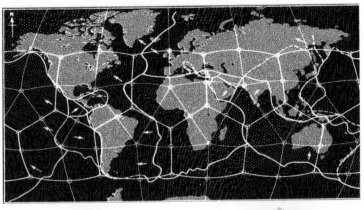

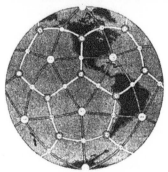
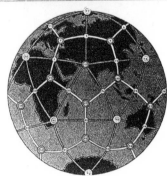

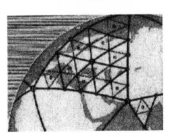

This page: Various versions of the Goncharov-Morozov-Makarov Earth-crystal grid. They claimed the lines and points of their grid matched many of the Earth's seismic fracture zones and ocean ridges, and also outlined worldwide atmospheric highs and lows, the paths of migratory animals, gravitational anomalies, and the sites of many ancient cities (after John Sinkiewicz). The geosynclinal areas that divide these platforms go along the edges between the triangles. Underwater mountain ridges in the oceans and the Earth's crust breaks usually go along or in parallel to the icosahedron ribs.

# PUTTING IT ALL TOGETHER
*the unified vector geometry projection*

---

In 1978, Professors William Becker and Bethe Hagens extended the Russian model, inspired by Buckminster Fuller's geodesic domes, into a grid based on the rhombic triacontahedron (*shown opposite right*), the dual of the icosidodecahedron Archimedean solid (see *Platonic & Archimedean Solids*, also in this series). The triacontahedron has 30 diamond-shaped faces, and possesses the combined vertices of the icosahedron and the dodecahedron. Their new model, which they later titled 'The Rings of Gaia', revealed 15 great circles, 120 scalene right-triangles (with no equal sides or equal angles) and 62 node-points. The great circles divided each rhombic face into four right-triangles. Although having no interest in Earth grids, Fuller had previously noticed these triangles and recorded their internal angles in planar and spherical notations (*shown below*).

The model was eventually developed into the 'Unified Vector Geometry' (UVG) projection, connecting all of the vertices of the five Platonic solids placed inside a sphere, using Fuller's 'great circle sets' from *Synergetics II*. A total of 121 great circles appeared, increasing the number of vertices to 4,862 (*see opposite page 1*). They proposed that the UVG grid could be a new geometrical model for Gaia.

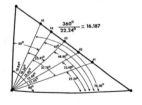
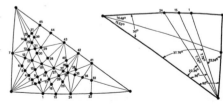

Above: The grid is oriented to the poles and north-south through Giza. Point 1 is located just north of Giza, near Behdet, a geodetic marker identified by Livio Stecchini.

Above: The grid based on the Rhombic Triacontahedron at the same orientation as the image above left. With 30 diamond (rhomb) faces, each with four triangles.

Above: The grid, showing pentagonal faces over Asia and Australasia. In total there are 12 pentagonal faces, 15 great circles, 62 vertices and 120 triangles.

Above: The grid duals that of the icosidodecahedron and shows truncated pentagonal faces. containing ten triangles, each having an approx 7:11:13 ratio.

# INTERESTING POINTS
*anomalies on the intersections*

The original Russian grid vertex numbering is preserved in the Becker and Hagens version shown below. Several ancient civilisations have thrived around certain grid points, but not many famous ancient sacred sites mark major vertices. Since c. 2,600 BC the Egyptians thrived around the Giza plateau [1], as did the inhabitants of the pyramidical complex at Caral in the northwest of Peru [35].

Photographic data collected by U.S. and Russian satellites confirm a fault line from Morocco to Pakistan (points 20 to 12). There are also circular geological structures 150-200 miles in diameter located at grid points 17 (Cerro Cubabi, a highpoint just south of the Mexico/U.S. border), 18 (Edge of continental shelf near Great Abaco Island in the Bahamas) and 20 (El Eglab, on edge of the Sahara desert, near Timbuktu). Grid points 49, southeast of Rio de Janeiro, and 27, in the Gulf of Carpentaria in northeast Australia, seem to have landmass forming around them, suggesting that these intersections could act as vortices of energy and shape the landscape over many millenia.

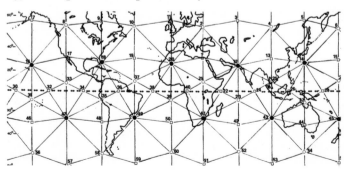

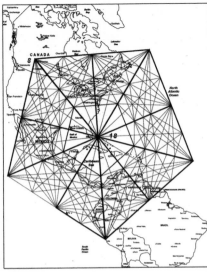

Left: Grid-points 8 and 18: Point 8 is near Buffalo Lake, Alberta, Canada. Large gas and oil reserves, major wheat farming, also with a 5000 year old 'medicine circle' near Majorville. Grid-point 18 is the centre of a pentagonal face with intersections. Large megalithic 'roads' have been discovered in Bimini, off the coast of Florida, suggesting a previous, yet unknown society, who could carve and transport large stones. It is also the northern tip of the Bermuda Triangle.

Below: Grid-point 17: Near the Organ Pipe National Monument. The ancient Hohokum people built immense irrigation canals here, their civilisation lasting some 9000 years. They made a ceremonial wine from the organ pipe cactus. This area marks the most sacred territory of the oldest native peoples in North America. There are small pyramids; rock art (some depicting a 'star explosion,' at White Tanks) and Mt. Pinacate. Once a major drug-trafficking area, it now home to an enormous communications dish array.

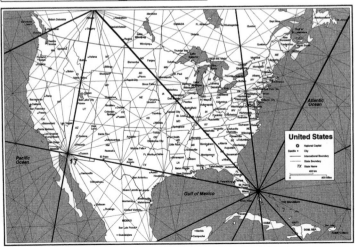

21

# HARTMANN AND CURRY GRIDS
## tools for the geopathically stressed

---

Geomancers have discovered several other global networks of energy. The first was discovered by Dr. Ernst Hartmann in the 1960s and runs magnetic N to S and E to W. It is a square grid spaced 5 ft 5 in apart, with lines 6-10 inches wide that rise vertically like invisible radioactive walls. When two lines cross, a 'Hartmann Knot' of geopathic stress occurs. Sleeping over crossings of double negative lines (which repeat at 115 ft intervals) have been known to cause nervous disturbances, headaches, cramps and rheumatism. Earthquakes distort this grid and a 50% increase in radioactivity has also been recorded at crossing points.

The Curry grid was discovered by Drs. Curry and Whitman in the 1970s and runs diagonally at 45° to north. The lines repeat every 8 ft SW to NE and 9 ft SE to NW. They are approx 2 ft wide, with double negative lines repeating every 164 ft. Considered more harmful than Hartmann knots, they are linked with sleep problems, depression and other nervous reactions.

Although these two grids are scientifically unproven, in 2006 Hans Giertz, a telecommunications expert, was able to determine their existence with low frequency electromagnetic energy experiments.

Similar grids include the Broad Curry grid that is 30° off north and the 'positive' double-Curry grid that is 20° off north with very wide intervals of 410 ft. Interestingly, this one is marked by megaliths, holy wells, chapels, hill forts and oak trees. In the 1980s R. Schneider discovered a grid at 45° with lines repeating every 965 ft. Shaun Kirwan has discovered the 'Angel Grid', that has huge etheric lines of force and relates to the golden section ratio. No doubt more will follow!

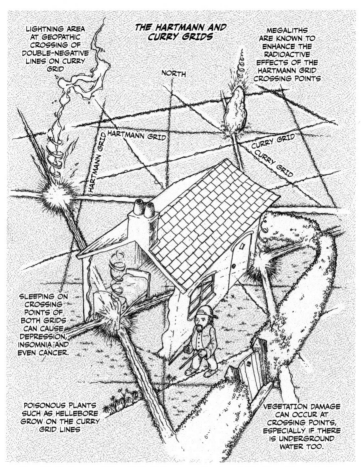

THE HARTMANN AND CURRY GRIDS

LIGHTNING AREA AT GEOPATHIC CROSSING OF DOUBLE-NEGATIVE LINES ON CURRY GRID

MEGALITHS ARE KNOWN TO ENHANCE THE RADIOACTIVE EFFECTS OF THE HARTMANN GRID CROSSING POINTS

NORTH

HARTMANN GRID    HARTMANN GRID

HARTMANN GRID

CURRY GRID

CURRY GRID

SLEEPING ON CROSSING POINTS OF BOTH GRIDS CAN CAUSE DEPRESSION, INSOMNIA AND EVEN CANCER.

POISONOUS PLANTS SUCH AS HELLEBORE GROW ON THE CURRY GRID LINES

VEGETATION DAMAGE CAN OCCUR AT CROSSING POINTS, ESPECIALLY IF THERE IS UNDERGROUND WATER TOO.

*Above: The Hartmann and Curry Grids. Both compress when stressed, depending on the severity of any trauma in the landscape. Under severe stress, such as old battle sites, the lines can be under 1ft apart. In these places the double negative knots are more frequent, and therefore more damaging to health. Geomancers say there are hundreds of grids that relate to all the different life forms and even elemental beings.*

23

# LANDSCAPE GEOMETRIES
*man-made patterns on earth*

Geometric grids may encircle Gaia, but looking more closely into the landscape, playful patterns turn up everywhere. For example, the capital of America, Washington DC, designed and constructed from 1791, has a layout suggesting knowledge of ancient metrology, sacred geometry and astronomy, later lost in the development of the city.

In Britain, an ancient 'national grid' of neolithic henge monuments, discovered by Robin Heath, links Arbor Low ('Stonehenge of the North'), Bryn Celli Ddu, an important burial chamber in north Wales, and Stonehenge. It displays a perfect 3:4:5 Pythagorean triangle.

Stonehenge also turns up in 'The Wessex Astrum', a landscape hexagram that is bisected by the St. Michael line. Interestingly, the line here between Stonehenge and Glastonbury is a tenth of the perimeter of the Circle of Perpetual choirs (*see page 7*). A landscape diamond (*top left*) aligns to the St. Michael axis and also to other sacred hills in the Somerset region, while a grid system and pentagonal geometry over the landscape in Rennes le Chateux in the south of France, connects churches, sacred hills and natural features (*shown below*).

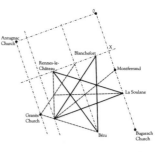

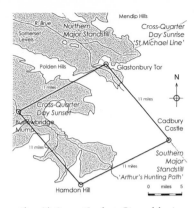

Above: The Somerset Landscape Diamond showing
the St. Michael Line and major lunar standstill
alignment (by N. Mann & P. Glasson, 2007)

Above: Golden section geometry underlies the design of
Washington DC. French architect, Pierre Charles L'Enfant
Plan of 1791, Library of Congress (by N. Mann, 2006)

Above: A geodetic grid (by R.Heath) which links
henge sites in the UK to form a Pythagorean triangle.
The base line corresponds to the Lunation triangle.

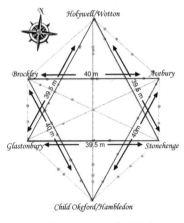

Above: The Wessex Astrum (by P. Knight,
T. Perrott) showing the St. Michael axis, distances
and several sacred hills on the lighter grey tone.

# GREAT CIRCLES ON EARTH
*cutting the world in two*

A *great circle* is a circle on a sphere whose centre lies at the centre of that sphere, so that it cuts it into two equal hemispheres. All longitudinal meridians are great circles. The equator is the only latitudinal great circle—all other latitudes form *lesser circles* on the globe. The UVG grid is composed entirely of great Earth circles, all 121 of them.

Below is shown Jim Alison's incredible great Earth circle, viewed along its equator. This formidable alignment takes in Nazca, Machu Picchu, Tassili n Ajjer, Siwa, Giza, Ur, Angkor Wat, Easter Island and many others. As we shall see in the pages that follow, there are other reasons to take specific notice of this alignment. Were the ancients conscious of this circle? Were they recording something? Shown top is a section of a great circle proposed by Robin Heath that takes in Stonehenge, Delphi, Giza, Mecca and the Ohio Serpent Mound.

In the 1980s, Glastonbury visionary Robert Coon produced an interesting planetary chakra map (*lower opposite*) with two great dragon-lines encircling the globe (he called the pair of them the 'Rainbow Serpent'). The British part of it aligns down the Michael-Mary lines (*see page 7*). The two currents do not form a perfect Earth circle but they do encircle the Earth.

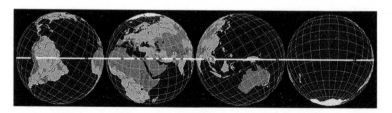

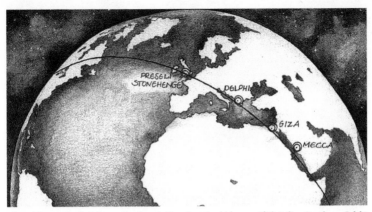

*Above:* The great Earth circle extending from the 'lunation triangle' (see page 7) that aligns Stonehenge, Delphi, Giza, Mecca, Ohio Serpent Mound, Sligo and the Preseli Bluestone site (by Janet Lloyd Davies, after R.Heath).

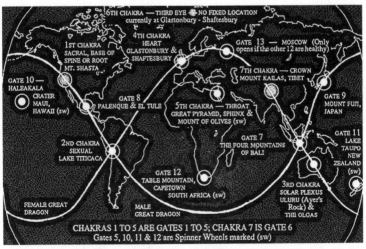

*Above:* Robert Coon's Rainbow Serpent travels the world from Uluru (Ayres Rock), linking 'planetary increase sites' or chakras, before meeting it back in Uluru. The Aborigines tell stories of a female snake Kuniya and her nephew Liru, who meet at Uluru. Dowsers have verified these energy lines in other parts of the world.

# THE PRIME MERIDIAN
*the centre of the world*

In October 1884, Professor Charles Piazzi Smythe, an avid Egyptologist and Astronomer Royal of Scotland, became involved in choosing the prime meridian of the Earth; zero degrees longitude.

There had already been other contenders. Paris was a possibility, but there was no fixed global agreement, so 25 countries met in Washington DC to decide on the location. At the meeting, Smythe proposed using the Great Pyramid, because great circles drawn north, south, east and west from Giza cover more land, as opposed to ocean, than from any other place on Earth (*opposite top*). The Great Pyramid was also perfectly aligned to the cardinal points of the compass, and sited at 30° above the equator. In the end, under some pressure, 22 countries voted for Greenwich, 31° 8' 8" west of Giza.

Previously, in the late 1700s, Napoleon's surveyors had used the cardinal points of the Great Pyramid to survey Lower Egypt, using a meridian as the baseline. They discovered that this cut the Delta region into two equal portions and that lines extended from the north corners of the Pyramid precisely enclosed the entire Delta (*lower opposite*).

It has been proposed that the Great Pyramid may also represent the northern hemisphere, suggesting the Egyptians accurately knew the size of the Earth. The height and perimeter of the Great Pyramid multiplied by 43,200 yields figures very close to the modern polar radius and equatorial circumference of the Earth. 43,200 is an important metrological number, $= 2^6 \times 3^3 \times 5^2$. The base length of the Great Pyramid is also precisely 1/8th of a minute of a degree of the Earth's polar circumference (a minute is 1/60th of a degree).

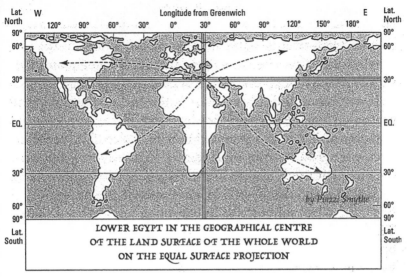

LOWER EGYPT IN THE GEOGRAPHICAL CENTRE
OF THE LAND SURFACE OF THE WHOLE WORLD
ON THE EQUAL SURFACE PROJECTION

*Above: Charles Piazzi Smythe's map showing the Giza Prime Meridian and landmass from Egypt.*
*Below left: Napoleon's survey of the Nile Delta. Below right: The Great Pyramid as the Earth's northern hemisphere*

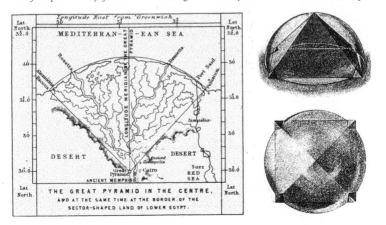

# LOCATING THE CENTRE
*the navel of the landscape*

The geodetic location of the Giza meridian echoes through other ancient cultures, who often sought to find the centre of their land or society. Nordic, Greek, Celtic and even Nazi traditions reveal a worldwide geomantic obsession with finding the exact centre of the homeland. The centre was seen as the birthplace of the tribe, the omphalus or 'navel of the world', an axis from which the king could survey his domain, and give laws from his sacred rock. These central places, whether stone circles, earthworks, hilltops or islets in rivers and lakes, functioned as 'moot' or 'ting' sites where national meetings were held 'under the light of the Sun'. John Michell also discovered that they were often located geographically at the centre of the most northerly-southerly and easterly-westerly axes (*shown below*).

Plato relates that the site of the symbolic centre must have the physical and spiritual qualities befitting a national omphalus. Were early surveyors also priestly diviners, masters of astronomy, geodesy and land measurement, as Caesar said of the British druids?

The two main British centres are the Isle of Man, the centre of the British Isles (*see opposite*), and Meriden in Warwickshire, the centre of England. The Romans named High Cross at Venonae the centre because it was equidistant from Hadrian's Wall and the Isle of Wight.

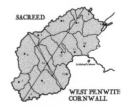

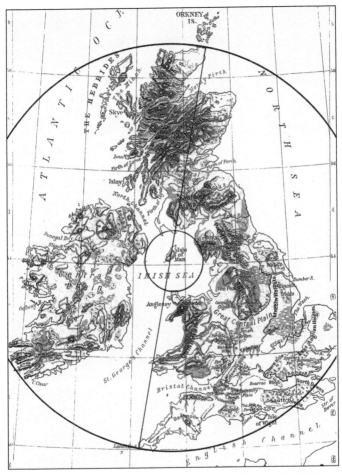

*Above: The main axis of the British Isles, from Duncansby Head in Scotland to Land's End in Cornwall, has its central point on the Isle of Man. The smaller circle of 100 miles in diameter, touches England, Wales, Ireland and Scotland (from "At the Centre of the World" by John Michell, 1994)*

# LANDSCAPE ZODIACS
*heavenly signs on earth*

In the 1920s Katherine Maltwood had a vision in which she perceived the signs of the zodiac overlaying the sacred landscape around Glastonbury, legendary burial place of King Arthur, and site of the first church in Europe. After plotting the figures on a map, twelve miles across, and noticing that earthworks, roads, and brooks outlined the astrological signs, she published a book: *Glastonbury's Temple of the Stars.* She found that street and village names hid tell-tale and long-lost clues. The Peruvian Nazca geoglyphs were being rediscovered at the same time, also possibly representing astrological signs.

Today, there are nearly 60 recorded terrestrial zodiacs in Britain, ranging from 10 (Ongar) to 32 (Pendle) miles wide. Some have 'dogs' as an extra sign, representing Canis Major, the 'Dog Star', spiritual guardian of the zodiac. No one is sure who built them, when, or if they are naturally formed, or just figments of over-active imaginations.

The famous St. Michael line mysteriously connects several zodiacs in southern England, clipping the edges of zodiacs at Bury St. Edmunds, Nuthampstead, Glastonbury, Bodmin Moor, and one in Cornwall.

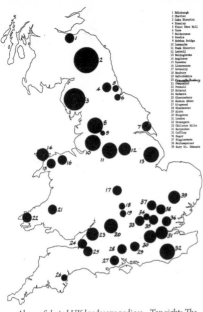

*Above: Selected UK landscape zodiacs. Top right: The Nuthampstead Zodiac, discovered by Nigel Pennick (the Michael line clips the NW of the Lion near Royston). Opposite page, left: The Glastonbury Zodiac. Opposite page, right: The Kingston Zodiac, drawn by Mary Caine. Below: A unicorn in the Glastonbury Zodiac which touches the Lion in Somerton, where the Lion and Unicorn coat of arms of Britain was created. Below: The Nuthampstead Zodiac, discovered by Nigel Pennick.*

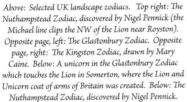

# MEASURING THE EARTH
*geodesy and ancient metrology*

The size and shape of the Earth has only been known for the last two centuries, but the ancients may have got there first. Measurement systems found at sites such as Stonehenge appear to be derived from an accurate understanding of the Earth's size, and builders of the ancient temples seem to have used this system to a high degree of accuracy.

In the ancient system, miles, cubits, feet and inches were all perfect subdivisions of the Earth's polar or equatorial circumference or its radius. For example, the meridian (polar) circumference is 24,883.2 miles, equal to 135,000,000 Roman feet, 63,000,000 Sacred cubits or 129,600,000 Greek feet (129,600 is the number of seconds in the 360 degrees of a circle). The values of the various ancient measures were grouped together by whole number ratios that relate to the English (geographic) foot, considered by some to be the 'root' of metrology.

The spheroid shape of the Earth means that degrees of latitude measured at the poles are longer than those at the equator. The average (mean) degree is 69.12 miles, a length quoted by Ptolemy (as 300,000 Roman remens) and which is still used officially today.

The canonical diameter of the Earth (7,920 miles) can be expressed as $8 \times 9 \times 10 \times 11$ miles. Likewise, the equatorial circumference (24,902.86 miles) is $360,000 \times 365.242$ English feet (also the number of days in a year), enabling space, time and angle to be worked out in either feet, days or degrees. The equatorial circumference relates to the meridian through the fraction 1261/1260 (*see other examples in table bottom right*). Various people have tried to explain how this could have been worked out in ancient times, but no one really knows!

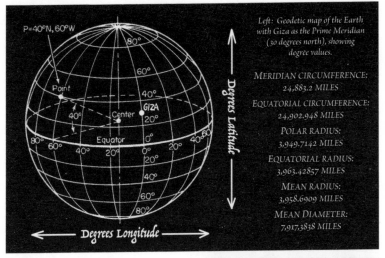

Left: Geodetic map of the Earth with Giza as the Prime Meridian (30 degrees north), showing degree values.

MERIDIAN CIRCUMFERENCE:
24,883.2 MILES

EQUATORIAL CIRCUMFERENCE:
24,902.948 MILES

POLAR RADIUS:
3,949.7142 MILES

EQUATORIAL RADIUS:
3,963.42857 MILES

MEAN RADIUS:
3,958.6909 MILES

MEAN DIAMETER:
7,917.3838 MILES

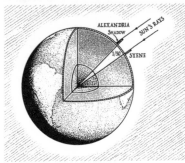

Above: Eratosthenes' [276-195 BC] experiment to measure the size of the Earth. He calculated the polar circumference to within 180 miles by noting the angle of a midday midsummer shadow in Alexandria. He knew that at Syene, 500 miles to the south, the midday midsummer Sun cast no shadow. The angle of the shadow at Alexandria was roughly 7 degrees, or one-fiftieth of 360, so 50 × 500 miles gave him 25,000 miles as the circumference (24,821 miles is the modern measurement).

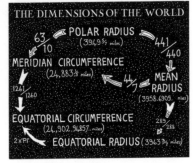

Above: The principal dimensions of the Earth from the study of ancient geodesy (courtesy Robin Heath, after John Neal). These numbers pop up frequently in metrology. For example, the Royal cubit identified by Petrie at the Great Pyramid differs as 441 to 440 to a Royal cubit of 12/7 English feet. The fractional relationships seem to have been known to the builders of ancient sacred sites.

# ANCIENT MAPS

### prehistoric mariners and perplexing projections

---

In 1513, a Turkish admiral, Piri Re'is, produced a map with a series of grid lines, compiled from twenty old charts and eight Mappa Mundis (*opposite top right*). Used for 200 years in the Mediterranean with no improvements, it was not until the 1960s that Charles Hapgood, an American historian, solved the projections used, replotted them, and came to the extraordinary conclusion that ancient seafarers must have sailed from pole to pole. In particular, Antarctica is often shown on the maps as two islands, or a large island with a smaller peninsula (*opposite lower right*), a fact only proven by radar survey through the ice in the late 20th century. Antarctica may have been surveyed when its coasts were free of ice, suggesting a possible date earlier than 12,000 BC.

Some maps had 'portolans' on them, like grid points, radiating out either 16 or 32 spokes, and these maps also showed accurate longitude, something not rediscovered until the 1700s by John Harrison. The prime meridian of the maps passed through Alexandria in Egypt, the ancient centre of learning where Piri Re'is had found many of them.

The Di Canestris map (*opposite top left*) shows an anthropomorphic king and queen representing North Africa and Europe, defining Alexandria at its centre. Hapgood found an interesting anomaly that Hagens picked up on: a 12-node perimeter containing 28 triangles corresponding closely to the UVG grid (*opposite lower left*).

In 1866, Leonce Elie de Beaumont, a founder of geology, published a map of France, centred on Paris and based on a pentagonal format. Often dismissed as 'arcane', it is precisely 1/12 of the Earth's surface, a dodecahedral face, fitting in neatly with modern grid theory.

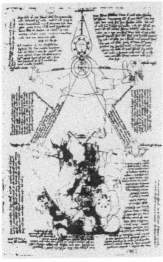

Above: The Dicanastris Map of 1335-1337, showing 'rhombic' geometry with four UVG grid triangles centred on Alexandria.

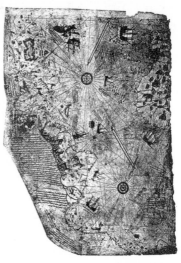

Above: The Piri Re'is Map. Accumulated from 20 old charts and global maps, known as Jaferiye by Arabs in the time of Alexander the Great.

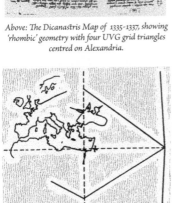

Above: A reprojection of a detail of the Di Canestris map showing the prime meridian through Alexandria and the UVG grid triangles.

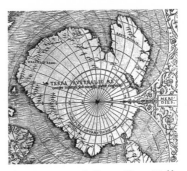

Above: Antarctica on the Oronteus Finaeus World Map of 1532. It was not until the mid 20th century that a modern survey was produced.

# LONGITUDE HARMONICS
*tuning into Giza*

---

Many ancient sacred sites can be arranged into a coherent pattern if Alexandria (or Giza, which is due south of it) defines the prime meridian. In 1998, author Graham Hancock developed a theory of the longitudinal distribution of sacred sites based on pentagonal geometry (*opposite top*). The massive Buddhist site of Angkor Wat is at a longitude 72° east of Giza, one fifth of the way round the globe.

Hancock's ideas may be extended. The Mayan sites of Copan, in Honduras, and Chitzen Itza, in Mexico, are both within half a degree of 120° west from Giza, one third of the way around the world. Was the geographic knowledge that the West acquired with the invention of the marine chronometer already in use thousands of years ago?

Strangely, the seat of the Church of England, Canterbury, is 30° west of Giza, one twelfth of a circle.

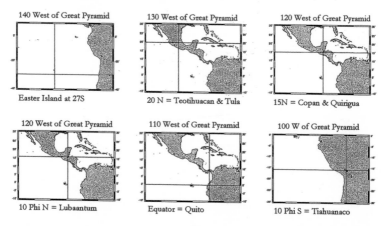

140 West of Great Pyramid

Easter Island at 27S

130 West of Great Pyramid

20 N = Teotihuacan & Tula

120 West of Great Pyramid

15N = Copan & Quirigua

120 West of Great Pyramid

10 Phi N = Lubaantum

110 West of Great Pyramid

Equator = Quito

100 W of Great Pyramid

10 Phi S = Tiahuanaco

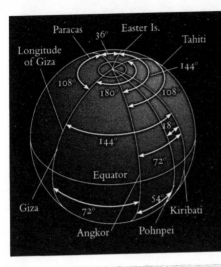

*Left: Graham Hancock's suggested theory of a world grid of intended longitudes with Giza as the meridian. Many of the sites encode pentagonal numbers such as 72° (1/5 around the planet). 108° is internal angle of a pentagon and 144 is 2/5ths of a circle.*

## HARMONIC LONGITUDES FROM GIZA

BAALBEK, LEBANON 5° E
*The world's largest megaliths*

ANGKOR WAT, CAMBODIA 72° E
*Major ancient Buddhist temple*

CHAVIN, PERU 108° W
*Shamanic megalithic temple complex*

THE PARACAS TRIDENT, PERU 108° W
*Nazca-like candleabra effigy*

TIAHUANACO, BOLIVIA 100° W
*Pyramid temple complex*

QUITO, ECUADOR 110° W
*Northern Inca capital*

CHICHEN ITZA AND COPAN 120° W
*Major Mayan capital cities*

TEOTIHUACAN, MEXICO 130° W
*Ancient Toltec and Mayan city*

EASTER ISLAND 140° W
*Megalithic statues facing east*

KIRIBATI, PACIFIC ISLANDS 144° E
*Ancient megalithic ruins*

## HARMONIC LONGITUDES TWIXT SITES

EASTER ISLAND TO ANGKOR WAT 144°
*two fifths of a circle*

ANGKOR WAT TO TAHITI 108°
*three tenths of a circle*

ANGKOR WAT TO KIRIBATI 72°
*one fifth of a circle*

ANGKOR WAT TO PARACAS 180°
*half a circle*

PARACAS TO EASTER ISLAND 36°
*one tenth of a circle*

STONEHENGE TO BOSNIAN PYRAMID 19.5°
*tetrahedral angle (see page 53)*

BOSNIAN PYRAMID TO MACHU PICCHU 90°
*a quarter of a circle*

NAN MADOL, POHNPEI TO ANGKOR 54°
*three twentieths of a circle*

CARNAC, BRITTANY TO YONAGUNI 120°
*one third of a circle*

See Appendix II for more information.

# LATITUDINAL HARMONICS
*secret sevens and stone circles*

---

Sacred sites were not only positioned at longitude harmonics. The massive 5,000-year-old Avebury stone circles are situated 51° 25' 43" north of the equator, exactly one seventh of a circle or 360/7° (also four sevenths of the quadrant between the equator and the north pole). The temples of Luxor (Thebes), Egypt, sit at 25° 25' 43", two sevenths of the quadrant distance. Supporting this analysis, the north African historian Ibn Khaldun [1332-1406], describes how the ancient world was divided into latitudinal sevenths in his *Muqaddimah*.

Getting into more localised detail, John Michell discovered in 2004 that while the latitude of Avebury is within the 52nd parallel (between 51° and 52° N), it is strangely exactly three sevenths of the way up. Furthermore, if the 52nd paralled is divided into 28 units (*opposite top right*) then the distance between Avebury and Stonehenge equals precisely seven of those units, 17.28 miles, or one quarter of a degree at that latitude (the Rollright Stones near Oxford mark the 52° latitude). The distance between Avebury and 52° is also 39.497142 miles, exactly 1/100th of the polar radius.

Interesting latitudes also occur between ancient Greek sites. Delphi, Dodona and Delos are all exactly one degree apart and lie along the path of the Apollo-St. Michael ley, angled at 60° (*lower opposite*). The line runs from Skellig St. Michael, in Ireland, and travels for 2,500 miles to Megiddo in Israel (Armageddon).

The notable cluster of stone circles in the Shetland Islands are found at 60° (one sixth of a circle), exactly twice Giza's 30° latitude (one twelfth of a circle). Coincidence or deliberate design?

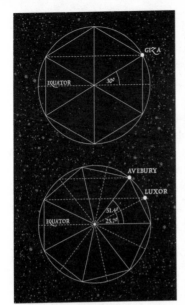

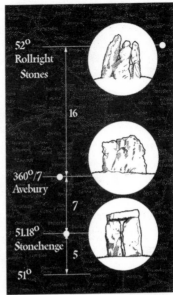

*Above left: Sites positioned at 6- and 7-fold divisions of Earth's quadrant (after Heath, Michell & Jacobs).*
*Above right: Avebury's position exactly three sevenths of the way between the 51st and 52nd parallel.*

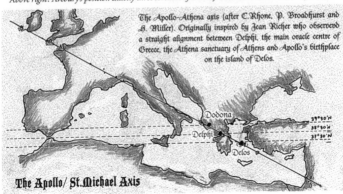

The Apollo-Athena axis (after C. Rhone, P. Broadhurst and H. Miller). Originally inspired by Jean Richer who observed a straight alignment between Delphi, the main oracle centre of Greece, the Athena sanctuary of Athens and Apollo's birthplace on the island of Delos.

The Apollo/St. Michael Axis

# GLOBAL POSITIONING
## lost codes of the ancients

---

Some ancient sites worldwide may have been built with knowledge of their exact location. Archaeocryptography, created by Carl Munck, uses the numbers of obvious features present at a site to produce the precise coordinates. For instance, the Kukulkan pyramid at Chichen Itza has 4 staircases, 4 corners, 365 steps (91 on each side plus an altar on top) and 9 terraces. These numbers multiplied together equal 52,560, a number encoded in Kukulkan's longitude west of Giza, 119°42' 10.51620648", for 119 × 42 × 10.51620648 = 52,560. Skeptics say he is just 'number crunching', selecting data to fit his results, but other commentators remain more enthusiastic.

Returning to Avebury, we find a similar 'code'. In 1996 John Martineau noticed two hidden corridors, defined by two unusual 'corners' of the henge, which align through the centres of the two inner stone circles. The angle between them is one seventh of a circle, 51° 25' 43", the precise latitude of the centre of the site. There are also exactly 72° of arc between Avebury and Chichen Itza, one fifth of the Earth's circumference.

Checking the distances and degrees between ancient sites produces some interesting results. Avebury is located 1/100th of the planetary circumference from the Hill of Tara and Newgrange, Ireland's largest megalithic structure (both 3,000 BC and 249.4 miles away). The Great Pyramid to Newgrange is 1/10th of a great circle (2,487.4 miles).

The Newark earthworks in Ohio are 6,000 miles from the Great Pyramid, and distances between them and nearby earthworks encode accurate astronomical geodesy (*see lower opposite, after James Q. Jacobs*).

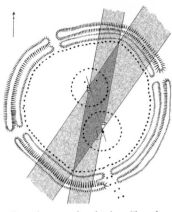

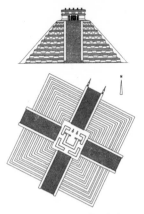

Above: The two corridors of Avebury. The angle between them equals the latitude of the site.

Above: Kukulkan pyramid at Chichen Itza. Latitude: 119°, 42,' 10.51620648"

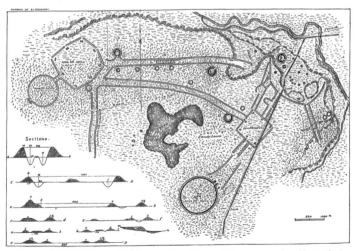

Above: 360° divided by the no. of days in a year (365.25636) equals the average number of degrees the Sun moves in a day, 0.98561°, a distance equal to that between Marietta Square and the Newark Octagon (above).

43

# OCTAGONS & HEXAGONS
## *some interesting alignments*

One of the most impressive geometrical earthworks in North America is the Newark Complex in Ohio. Its vast scale has now been overtaken by the local town and a golf course, but, to put it in perspective, the Great Pyramid of Giza would easily fit within the octagon (*opposite top*). James Q. Jacobs noticed that its orientation is 51.4° east of true north, a seventh of a circle, and also the latitude of Avebury in England (51.42°).

Geomancer Cort Lindahl followed the complex's orientation and found that its NW-SW axis points directly to the Great Pyramid, 6,008 miles away. Was it connected to both the megalith builders of England, and the pyramid builders of Egypt? Newark also encodes advanced astronomical alignments, most notably, how the octagon's eight sides encode the different aspects of the 18.6-year moon cycle.

After crossing the Atlantic ocean, the line goes through Europe and hits several mounds, megaliths and temples in France, Italy, Greece and Crete, plus through the ancient Egyptian city of Alexandria. Strangely, it goes through another octagonal construction in Voletta, Italy. The Baptistery of San Giovanni was constructed in 13th century and sits within an ancient megalithic landscape once ruled by the Pelasgians and Etruscans, the architects responsible for the polygonal walls.

The temple of Jupiter at Baalbek in Lebanon also connects to the Great Pyramid. Featuring the largest megalithic blocks in the world, the northeast edge of Baalbek's hexagonal platform aligns precisely with the NE to SW diagonal of the Great Pyramid (407 miles away). Were both Newark and Baalbek specifically oriented to the Great Pyramid?

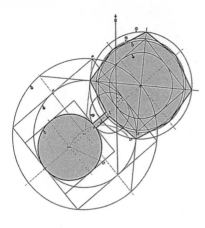

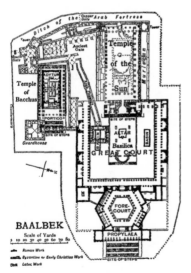

Left: The secret geometrical construction of Newark Earthworks, Ohio, USA. Its NW-SE axis points directly to the Great Pyramid in Egypt and hits several other ancient sites on the way, including Alexandria (see too previous page, 42-43).

Left: Plan of the ancient temple of Baalbek, Lebanon showing the unusual hexagon in the east whose north-western side points directly to the Great Pyramid. Above: Entrance to the Temple of the Sun. Below: A 1,242 ton stone at Baalbek.

45

# GOLDEN SECTION SITES
*a web of phi*

---

The golden section is a proportion found in pentagrams, icosahedra, dodecahedra and throughout nature. Some researchers have observed golden ratios in the distances between sacred sites thousands of miles apart, suggesting a possible ancient use of it in surveying the planet.

Jim Alison, for example, discovered in the 1990s that along his impressive great circle alignment (*see page 26*) Angkor Wat is 4,745 miles from the Great Pyramid, which is 7,677 miles from Nazca, the two distances being in the golden ratio (0.618 or 1.618), as 4,745 × 1.618 = 7,677 (*see below and top right*). Alison also found that distances (in miles) between sites hid Fibonacci sequence numbers. For example, Giza to Nazca is 7,692 miles and Nazca to Angkor is 12,446 miles (the 360th Fibonnaci number is 76,924, and the 361st is 12,446).

In the same vein, Rand Flem-Ath found that the White pyramid near Xian, China, is located between the north pole and equator at 34° 26' N, which divides the quadrant into the golden ratio: 3,840 (miles from the north pole) × 1.618 = 6,213 (miles in a quadrant). Flem-Ath also found numerous sites close to the latititude 10 × 1.618°, or 16° 11' north and south of the equator. Sites at these latitudes include Tiahuanaco (16°38' N) and Lubaantum (16° 17' N), as well as those shown in the table on the opposite page.

ANGKOR WAT      GIZA      NAZCA

|← 4,745 MILES →|← 7,677 MILES →|

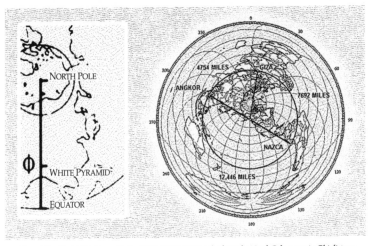

*Above left : The White Pyramid sits at 34° 26' N. 3,840 miles from the North Pole, a precise Phi distance*
*Above right: Projection of phi distances from Jim Alison's great circle. Below: TheWhite pyramid, nr. Xian, China*

10 PHI FROM EQUATOR (16° 11'):  16°1.7'N - LUBAANTUM,  16° 38'N - TIAHUANACO,  16° 50'S - RAIATEA.

10 PHI POLE TO POLE (21° 15'N):  20° 40' - CHICHEN ITZA,  21° 30' - WABAR TEKTITE.

10 PHI POLE TO EQUATOR (34° 23'N):  34.00° - BAALBEK,  34°19' - EHDIN ,  34° 22' - XIAN PYRAMIDS.

10 PHI EQUATOR TO POLE (55° 37'N):  55° 40' - KILWINNING (MASONIC CENTRAL),  55° 52' - ROSSLYN

*Above:  Various 'sacred latitudes' using different golden quadrant and hemispherical divisions.*

# THE SHIFTING GRID
*surface slippage and the old pole*

As well as studying ancient maps, Charles Hapgood (*see page 36*) made the suggestion that the Earth's crust "... much as the skin of an orange, if it were loose, might shift over the inner part of the orange all in one piece". It was already known that the inner flippings of the iron-rich core of the Earth caused magnetic pole reversals (recorded in the rock of the mid-Atlantic ridge, *see page 2*). In addition to this, Hapgood radically proposed that the rigid, stony outer shell of the Earth, the lithosphere, might occasionally slide over the top of the lubricating layer, the asthenosphere. One result of this theory is that there are no 'Ice Ages' as such, instead the movement of the pole causes different areas to be covered in ice at different times.

Any movement of this sort would probably cause major worldwide devastation, and Rand Flem-Ath believes this happened between 11-12,000 years ago when the poles moved 30° to their current positions from the Hudson Bay pole (*see below*).

Albert Einstein supported Hapgood's theory, and suggested that the build-up of weight of the ice-caps could cause such a shift to occur over periods from a few thousand years to only a few days!

 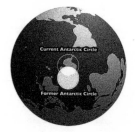

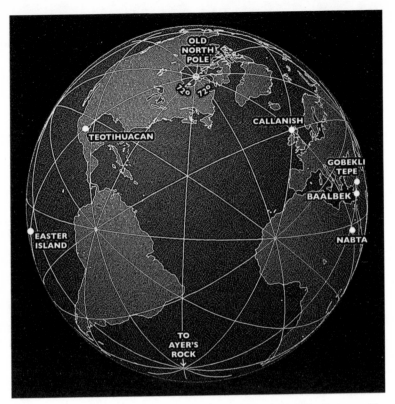

Above: A suggestive world grid, centred on the old North Pole in Hudson Bay (60°N 83°W), taking in some of the most ancient sites on the planet [produced by the author with J. Martineau's World Grid Program]. Easter Island and Lhasa both sit precisely on the old equator (Lhasa on a node point). Nabta is the oldest stone circle found to date. Gobekli Tepe is the oldest city yet discovered and Baalbek has the largest megaliths in the world. Giza, Jericho, and Nazca were all at 15° N. British sites such as Stonehenge and Rosslyn also point to the old pole position (50,000-12,000 years ago). The angle between the old and new poles from Stonehenge is 46° degrees and its latitude back then was 46° N, a 46/46 site. Similarly, Rosslyn in Scotland is a 50/50 site. In fact, from the Hudson Bay pole, there are over 60 ancient sites all within half a degree of 'sacred latitudes' probably five times what we have today. Were the ancient surveyors recording the previous polar displacement and how damaging it had been, setting up a series of interrelated measuring points around the world so they could measure future slippages?

# EARTH MUSIC
*cymatics, sferics, tweeks and whistlers*

The Earth is very noisy. It gives off a relentless symphony of countless notes imperceptible to the human ear. Seismometers can detect the Earth's 'hum', colossal mysterious ring-like oscillations or waves, that have been compared to the *aum* sound of Hindu creationism. The aurora, or 'northern lights', also emit shrieks and whistles into space (known as auroral kilometric radiation) when charged particles from the solar wind hit the Earth's magnetic field.

If humans had radio antennae as ears, we would hear lightning strikes emit a broadband pulse of radio waves. These 'sferics', 'tweeks' and 'whistlers' travel around the world by bouncing back and forth between the surface and the ionosphere, striking somewhere on the planet roughly 100 times per second, sometimes moving along magnetic flow lines. Combined with earthquakes, volcanoes, moving water and high force winds, could this symphony somehow organise the energies of the Earth into a coherent vibrating geometric grid?

The study of how sound affects matter is called 'cymatics', named after the Greek *kymatika* (matters pertaining to waves). Dr. Hans Jenny, a student of Buckminster Fuller, conducted clever experiments, in which a droplet of water containing a very fine suspension of light-coloured particles (a colloidal suspension) was vibrated at various diatonic musical frequencies. He photographed complicated geometries appearing inside the droplets, surrounded by elliptical lines connecting their nodes. High vibrations created the most complex designs, and different mediums affected the results. Jenny's work demonstrated the reality of sound forming physical phenomena.

*Above, left to right: Cymatic vibrational circles produced on the faces of an icosahedron, octahedron and dodecahedron.*

*Above: Cymatic forms based on Hans Jenny's photographs of light passing through vibrated water, sometimes using two tones. 3-D grid-like forms appear, with 12-, 3- and 6-fold geometry.*

*Above: Also redrawn from Hans Jenny's photographs. Turpentine vibrated on a film creating grid-like patterns similar to the Hartmann and Curry grids (page 22).*

# GEOMETRY ON OTHER PLANETS

*energy patterns everywhere*

In 1972 distinguished planetologist Dr. Robert Duncan-Enzmann suggested that tetrahedral geometry might define the locations of large scale energy upwellings on planets throughout the solar system. Tetrahedra with vertices at the poles define latitudes 19.47° above and below the equator. Olympus Mons (a Martian volcano three times larger than Mount Everest, and the highest mountain in the solar system) is found at this latitude, as is the most active volcano on Earth, Kilauea, in Hawaii. Further phenomena around 19.5° include increased solar flare activity on the surface of the Sun (*opposite top*) and the dark bands of clouds around Saturn.

There are many other examples of planetary geometries. Jupiter's great 'Red Spot' is found at 22.5°, a quarter of a quadrant distance. This is the same latitude as a similar 'great dark spot' on Neptune, accompanied by a thin band of white clouds circling the planet, which was discovered in June 1994 by NASA. The Neptune spot completely disappeared in April 1995, but it soon reappeared, this time in Neptune's northern hemisphere, again at 22.5° with identical banding! NASA noted that it was a "near-mirror image of the first spot".

In 1981, scientists were astonished to discover a stationary 'cymatic' hexagon, twice the size of the Earth, at Saturn's north pole, with multi-tiered linear clouds bands swirling around it. Uranus' moon Miranda displays huge triangular features that ressemble the faces of an icosahedron, and other polygonal areas (superimposed pentagonal and hexagonal) which seem to shape the terrain. Is it really too much to imagine energetic geometries might also exist on Earth?

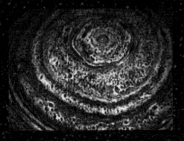

Top left: Tetrahedra inside a sphere defines 19.5°
latitudes above and below the equator.
Above right: The Sun has increased solar flare activity
at 19.5° above and below the equator.
Centre: Duncan-Enzmann noticed that the Olympus
Mons volcano on Mars sits at 19.5° north, defined
by a tetrahedral vertice.
Left: The hexagon at Saturn's north pole retains
its integrity and has been visible since its discovery
in 1981 (courtesy of NASA).

# NATURAL GRIDS
## *waterfalls, volcanoes and mountains*

---

Natural sites like volcanoes and waterfalls may also be involved in grid systems. Two of the world's largest waterfalls, Victoria Falls in Africa and Angel Falls in Venezuela, are located precisely 90° apart, forming two vertices of an octahedron which also aligns to the pyramids of Giza (*opposite top left*). Another octahedron (*top right*), connects the world's most active volcano, Kilauea in Hawaii with Angkor Wat and Nazca. Kilauea sits beside the world's largest volcano, Mauna Loa, both at 19.5°N, involving tetrahedral geometry (*previous page*). Two other great circles pass through Kilauea and important waterfalls and mountains (*opposite, lower left*). A newly discovered great Earth circle joins Giza, Lhasa and the megalithic islands of Tonga. Tonga and Hawaii have both been proposed as centres of the pre-Atlantian Pacific Lemurian civilisation!

Some of the more controversial claims about the Earth grid involve UFO flight-paths, antigravity and time-travel. In 1943, during the Philadelphia Experiment, the USS Eldridge reportedly 'vanished' into a strange mist as it was transported 200 miles to the Norfolk docks and back again, via a pulsating magnetic field. Coral Castle, a megalithic village in Florida near grid-point 18, was built in the 1930s and 40s by Ed Leedskalnin, who single-handedly quarried, carved and lifted over 1,100 tons of rock with no modern tools. Strange vortices of energy, time dilations, light phenomena and gravitational anomalies have been observed at grid points all over the world.

Ultimately the Earth grid remains a mystery. Whether an artifact of subtle energies, ancient wizards, aliens or the human imagination, it can take one on an amazing journey to some incredible places.

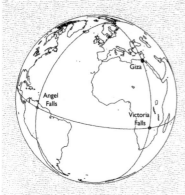

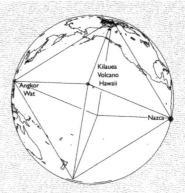

Above: Angel Falls (Kerepakupai merú), the world's highest free-falling waterfall at 3,212 ft, is 90° from the Victoria Falls or Mosi-oa-Tunya (the Smoke that Thunders), the second largest (after Martineau).

Above: Kilauea is one of five shield volcanoes that form the Islands of Hawaii. It has been active continuously since January 1983 and sits aside Mauna Loa, the world's largest volcano.

Above: Mt. Shasta has been identified by various groups as a cosmic power point, a UFO landing spot, a Lemurian sanctury, a gateway to the fifth dimension and a source of magic crystals!

Above: A great Earth circle connecting Giza, Lhasa and Tonga, three major ancient capitals that stretch back into pre-history and were considered 'sacred centres' of their cultures.

1) **31.72°N 31.20°E**
   On the Egyptian continental shelf, at approximately the midpoint between the two outlets of the Nile at Masabb Rashid and Masabb Dumyat. Very close to Behdet.

2) **52.62°N 31.20°E**
   On the Sozh River east of Gomel, at the boundary junction of Ukraine, Belarus, and Russia. Numerous megalithic sites and Venus figurines from Paleolithic era found.

3) **58.28°N 67.20°E**
   In marshy lowlands just west of Tobolsk

4) **52.62°N 103.20°E**
   In the lowlands north of the southern tip of Lake Baykal, at the edge of highlands

5) **58.28∞N 139.20∞E**
   In the highlands along the coast of the Sea of Okhotsk

6) **52.62°N 175.20°E**
   Slightly east of Attu at the western tip of the Aleutian Islands

7) **58.28°N 148.80°W**
   Edge of continental shelf in the Gulf of Alaska

8) **52.62°N 112.80°W**  Buffalo
   Lake, Alberta, at the edge of highlands in lowlands

9) **58.28°N 76.80°W**
   Just east of Port Harrison on Hudson's Bay

10) **52.62°N 40.80°W**
    Gibbs Fracture Zone

11) **58.28°N 4.80°W**
    Loch More on the north-west coast of Scotland

12) **26.57°N 67.20°E**
    On the edge of the Kirthar Range bordering the Indus River Valley, directly north of Karachi

13) **31.72°N 103.20°E**
    At the east edge of the Himalayas in Szechuan Province, just west of the Jiuding Shan summit

14) **26.57°N 139.20°E**
    At the intersection of Kydshu Palau Ridge, the West Mariana Ridge, and the Iwo Jima Ridge

15) **31.72°N 175.20°E**
    At the intersection of Hess Plateau, the Hawaiian Ridge, and the Emperor Seamounts

16) **26.57°N 148.80°W**
    Northeast of Hawaii, midway between the Murray Fracture Zone and the Molokai Fracture Zone

17) **31.72°N 112.80°W**
    Cerro Cubabi, a highpoint just south of the US/Mexico border near Sonoita and lava fields

18) **26.57°N 76.80°W**
    Edge of continental shelf near Great Abaco Island in the Bahamas

19) **31.72°N 40.80°W**
    Atlantis Fracture Zone

20) **26.57°N 4.80°W**
    In El Eglab, a highland peninsula at the edge of the Sahara Desert sand dunes

21) **10.81°N 31.20°E**
    Sudan Highlands, edge of White Nile marshfields

22) **0° 49.20°E**  Somali
    Abyssal Plain

23) **10.81°S 67.20°E**
    Vema Trench (Indian Ocean) at the intersection of the Mascarene Ridge, the Carlsberg Ridge, and Maldive Ridge into the MidIndian Ridge

24) **0° 85.20°E**
    Ceylon Abyssal Plain

25) **10.81°N 103.20°E**
    Kompong Som. a natural bay on the southern coast of Cambodia southwest of Phnom Penh

26) **0° 121.20°E**
    At the midpoint of Teluk, Tomini, a bay in the northern area of Sulawesi

27) **10.81°S 139.20°E**
    Midpoint of the mouth of the Gulf of Carpentaria

28) **0° 157.20°E**
    Centre of the Solomon Plateau

29) **10.81°N 175.20°E**
    Midpoint of the vast abyssal plain between Marshall Islands, Mid-Pacific Mountains, and the Magellan Plateau

30) **0° 166 80°W**
    Nova Canton Trough

31) **10.81°S 148.80°W**
    Society Islands

32) **0° 130.80°W**
    Galapagos Fracture Zone

33) **10.81°N 112.80°W**
    East end of the Clipperton Fracture Zone

34) **0° 94.80°W**
    Junction of the Coeos Ridge & the Carnegie Ridge, just west of Galapagos Islands.

35) **10.81°S 76.80°W**
    Lake Punrrun in Peruvian coastal highlands

36) **0° 58.80°W**
    State of Amazonas. At tip of minor watershed highlands

37) **10.81°N 40.80°W**
    Vema Fracture Zone

38) **0° 22.80°W**
    Romanche Fracture Zone

39) **10.81°S 4.80°W**
    Edge of Mid-Atlantic Ridge in Angola Basin, just southeast of Ascension Fracture Zone

40) **0° 13.20°W**
    Gabon highlands, at intersection of three borders

*Grid Points from William Becker & Bethe Hagens,
as based upon their UVG Planetary Grid model.*

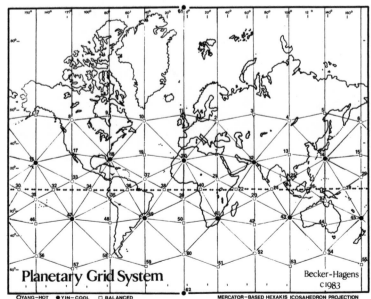

**Planetary Grid System**

Becker-Hagens
c1983

○ YANG—HOT  ● YIN—COOL  □ BALANCED          MERCATOR—BASED HEXAKIS ICOSAHEDRON PROJECTION

# APPENDIX II
## latitudes & longitudes of selected sites

Alexandria - 31°11'53"N, 29°59'09" E

Angkor Wat - 13°24' 45"N, 103°52' 01"E

Arbor Low - 53°10'08"N, 1°45'42"W

Avebury - 51°25'43"N, 1°51'09"W

Baalbek - 34°0'25"N, 36°12' 11"E

Babylon - 32°32'32"N, 44°25'15"E,

Bimini (north) - 25°46'0"N, 79°16'43"W

Bosnian Pyramids - 43°58'37"N, 18°10'41"E

Bryn Celli Ddu - 53°12'28"N, 4°14'05"W

Canterbury - 51°16'45"N, 1°05'03"E

Caral - 10°53'28"N, 77°31'24"E

Callanish - 58°11'51"N, 6°44'42"W

Carnac, Brittany - 47°34'17"N, 2°57'01"W

Chavin - 9°36'47"N, 77°13'58"W

Chichen Itza - 20°40'59"N, 88°34'07"W

Copan - 14°51'30"N, 2°57'05"W

Coral Castle - 25°30'02"N, 80°26'40"W

Cuzco - 13°31'06"S, 78°51'48"W

Delphi - 38°28'53"N, 22°29'46"E

Easter Island - 27°07'20"N, 109°21'05"W

Giza - 29°58'45"N, 31°08'03"E

Glastonbury Tor - 53°08'39"N, 2°41'50"W

Gobekli Tepe - 37°13'26"N, 38°55'21"E

Jericho - 31°51'01"N, 35°26'10"E

Jerusalem - 31°46'15"N, 35°13'20"E

Kilauea - 19°25'12"N, 155°17'24"W

Knossos - 35°17'52"N, 25°09'48"E

Knowth - 53°42'04"N, 6°29'28"W

Lhasa - 29°40'02"N, 91°10'10"E

Long Meg - 54°43'41"N, 2°40'02"W

Luxor - 25°42'00"N, 32°38'22"E

Machu Picchu - 13°09'50"S, 72°32'46"W

Mecca - 21°25'38"N, 39°48'53"E

Mohenjo-Daro - 27°19'31"N, 68°08'00"E

Nabta - 22°30'29"N, 30°43'32"E

Nan Madol - 6°50'41"N, 158°20'06"E

Nazca - 14°41'31"S, 75°09'00"W

Newark Octagon - 40°03'17"N, 82°26'39"W

Newgrange - 53°41'41"N, 6°28'30"W

Ohio Serpent Mound - 39°01'30"N, 83°25'41"W

Ollantaytambo - 13°15'26"S, 72°16'02"W

Paracas - 13°51'10"S, 76°17'50"W

Quito - 13°46'47"S, 78°31'27"W

Rennes le Chateux - 28°52'11"N, 42°53'57"E

Rollright Stones - 51°58'33"N, 1°34'15"W

Rosslyn - 55°52'21"N, 3°07'12"W

Saqqara - 29°52'17"N, 31°12'49"E

Silbury Hill - 51°24'56"N, 1°51'24"W

St.Michael's Mount - 50°06'26"N, 5°29'12"W

Stonehenge - 51°10'43"N, 1°49'30"W

Tara - 53°34'46"N, 6°36'42"W

Teotihuacan - 19°41'33"N, 98°50'38"W

Tiahuanaco - 16°33'24"S, 68°40'22"W

Tikal - 17°13'23"N, 89°37'24"W

Tonga - 21°08'12"S, 175°02'53"W

Troy - 39°57'28"N, 26°14'18"E

Ur - 30°57'46"N, 46°06'11"E

Wandlebury - 52°9'29" N, 0°10'58"E

Xian Pyramid - 34°16'13"N, 108°49'02"E

Yonaguni - 24°17'47"N, 123°50'37"E